Waltham Forest Libraries

Please return this item by the last dat~~e~~
renewed unless required by

D0314655

17/12/18		
	X	

Need to renew your books?
http://www.walthamforest.gov.uk/libraries or
Dial 0333 370 4700 for Callpoint – our 24/7 automated telephone renewal
line. You will need your library card number and your PIN. If you do not
know your PIN, contact your local library.

'Greedy Birds'
An original concept by Gary Sheppard
© Gary Sheppard

Illustrated by Tim Budgen

Published by MAVERICK ARTS PUBLISHING LTD

Studio 3A, City Business Centre, 6 Brighton Road,

Horsham, West Sussex, RH13 5BB

© Maverick Arts Publishing Limited November 2018

+44 (0)1403 256941

A CIP catalogue record for this book is available at the British Library.

ISBN 978-1-84886-384-2

www.maverickbooks.co.uk

Green

This book is rated as: Green Band (Guided Reading)
The original picture book text for this story has been
modified by the author to be an early reader.

GREEDY
BIRDS

by Gary Sheppard

illustrated by
Tim Budgen

Mavis was very kind.

She loved to cook and to share.

One morning a hungry bird sat on
her shed. She threw it some bread.

The next day there were two birds.

She cooked the birds some buns.

Soon…

...the garden was full of birds waiting to be fed!

There were greedy gannets,

chubby crows,

...plump pigeons,
and lots more.

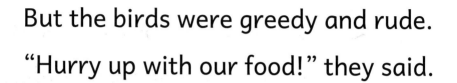

But the birds were greedy and rude.

"Hurry up with our food!" they said.

"Can you please wait?" Mavis asked.

But the birds got greedier and ruder.

And Mavis got sadder.

Then she had an idea...

...she started making the biggest pie you've ever seen!

"Come into the kitchen," Mavis said to the birds.

"Just cover your eyes and stand over there."

"Mmm!" said the birds,
and in they went.

"I've made you a dish called
Birdie Surprise," said Mavis.

When the birds opened their eyes they were inside... a GIANT pie!

"Surprise!" said Mavis.

"Let us out!" said the birds.

"Only if you promise to be nice," said Mavis. "I need your help to open my dream pie shop."

"We'll do it!" said the birds.

And they did.

All of the birds worked with Mavis
to bake lots of tasty pies.

It was a great success!

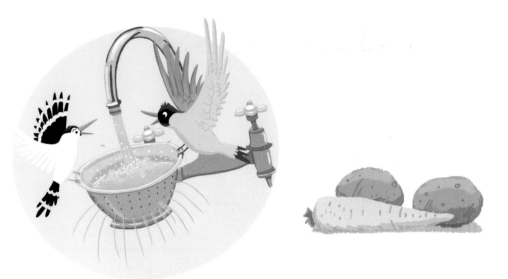

Before long
the shop was open.

Lots of people came to buy the pies!

Mavis's dream had come true.

She gave the birds as much pie as
they wanted to thank them for
their help.

Quiz

1. What two things does Mavis love to do?
a) Swim and jump
b) Dance and sing
c) Cook and share

2. What does Mavis not feed to the birds?
a) Bread
b) Chips
c) Pie

3. Why does Mavis feel sad?
a) She has no bread left
b) The birds are greedy and rude
c) Lots of people buy her pies

4. When the birds opened their eyes they were inside... a _____!

a) Big car

b) Nice garden

c) Giant pie

5. What is Mavis's dream?

a) To open a pie shop

b) To open a zoo

c) To eat lots of pie

Turn over for answers

Book Bands for Guided Reading

The Institute of Education book banding system is a scale of colours that reflects the various levels of reading difficulty. The bands are assigned by taking into account the content, the language style, the layout and phonics. Word, phrase and sentence level work is also taken into consideration.

Maverick Early Readers are a bright, attractive range of books covering the pink to white bands. All of these books have been book banded for guided reading to the industry standard and edited by a leading educational consultant.

To view the whole Maverick Readers scheme, visit our website at

www.maverickearlyreaders.com

Or scan the QR code above to view our scheme instantly!

Quiz Answers: 1c, 2b, 3b, 4c, 5a